It's Always Been You

Morgan Burke

Illustrated by Julia Anne Adams

For orders, please visit www.morganburkewrites.com
For prints of paintings, visit www.jwadamsfineart.com

Cover design and book formatting by Jenny Zandona
Illustrations by Julia Anne Adams
Hardback ISBN 978-1-7360957-0-6
Paperback ISBN 978-1-7360957-1-3
eBook ISBN 978-1-7360957-2-0

Library of Congress Control Number: 2020922388.

Burke, Morgan
It's Always Been You/ Morgan Burke

It's Always Been You is a poetic, artistic rendering of a mother's
love story to her child. The message of the book reveals the
"greatest secret of them all," the reality that within and all around
her child there is a love bigger than anything they could imagine.
ISBN-(hc) 978-1-7360957-0-6

To Claire, Heather, Caleb and Jayden

May you always see the world

with eyes of wonder.

My little one, my little love,

You are a gift from
heaven above.

I'll hold you now while you are small,
and tell you the greatest secret of them all.

Though I can't imagine how it could be,
there is one who loves you more than me.

While we prayed and dreamed of a life we would share, He was knitting you together with delicate care.

He's been there all along and His love is the song that I sing as I rock you to sleep.

It's in the warmth of your blanket
wrapped around you so tight,

And in the softness of the way that
I kiss you goodnight.

His love, you'll soon see is in the sky, in the tree, as its leaves rustle quiet in the wind.

It's in the beauty you'll find in flowers of every kind, as He smiles and says, "They're for you."

His love is grand
and He'll hold your hand

As your feet learn to walk,
skip and run.

Then finally, one night
as you behold the sight
of the stars in their grand display

He will take such delight
as you ponder their height
and about what makes
night turn to day.

"It's me," He'll whisper
and your heart will say "It's true."
It could only, ever, always be You.

About the Author and Illustrator

Morgan Burke is a mom, former special education teacher and a writer. She enjoys writing about adoption and the hard stuff of motherhood as a way of processing the fast-moving world around her.

Being in nature, baking, and spending time with her family are the things that bring her joy.

She lives in Huntsville, Alabama with her husband and two toddler boys.

Learn more about Morgan at www.morganburkewrites.com.

An artist most of her life, Julia Anne Adams has studied in the United States and Italy, from The Florence Academy of Art to studios in Philadelphia, San Francisco and Alabama.

She believes that every day in the studio provides an opportunity to express God's love for us. Her desire is to capture the beauty of His creation in every painting.

Julia Anne lives with her husband and daughter in Huntsville, Alabama. They are expecting another little girl to join the family soon.

You can find more of Julia Anne's work or purchase prints of her illustrations at www.jwadamsfineart.com.

CPSIA information can be obtained
at www.ICGtesting.com
Printed in the USA
LVHW072108171220
674452LV00010B/32